Food & Snac

Coloring Book For

Adults & Kids

Dive into the world of gastronomic delights.

"Food & Snacks Coloring Book For Adults & Kids" is designed for everyone from young enthusiasts to seasoned artists. Relax with the calming outlines of cakes, vibrant allure of fruits, and rustic charm of vegetables. Whether you're taking a moment for yourself or spending time with your family, these pages are your canvas for relaxation and fun. Dive into each design, let your imagination swirl around.

Happy coloring!

ISBN: 9798323404742

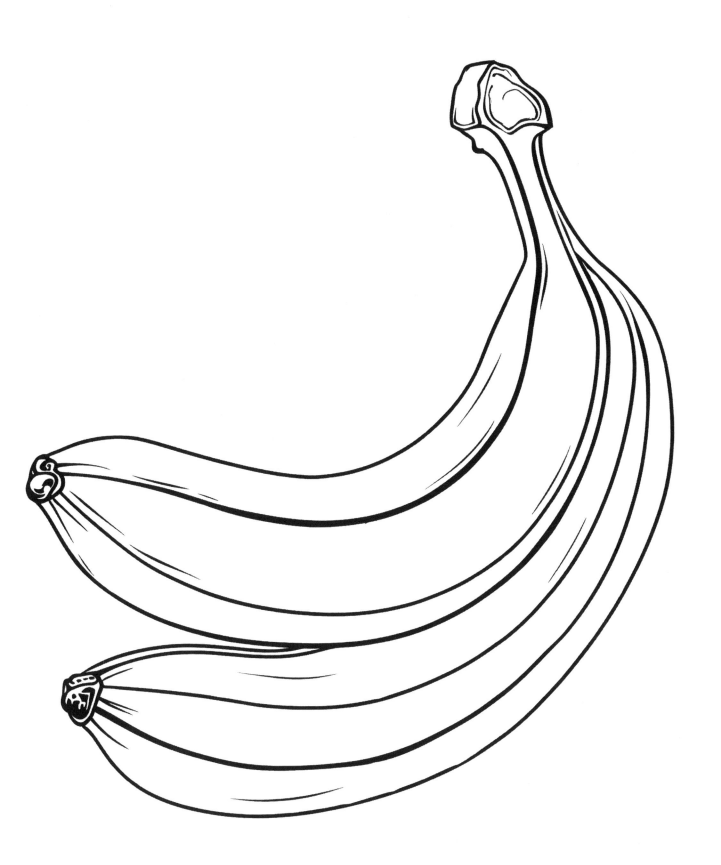

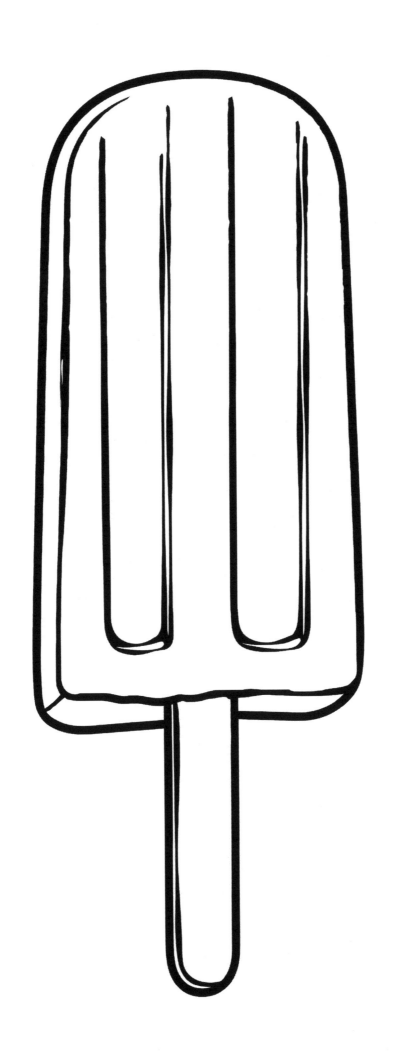

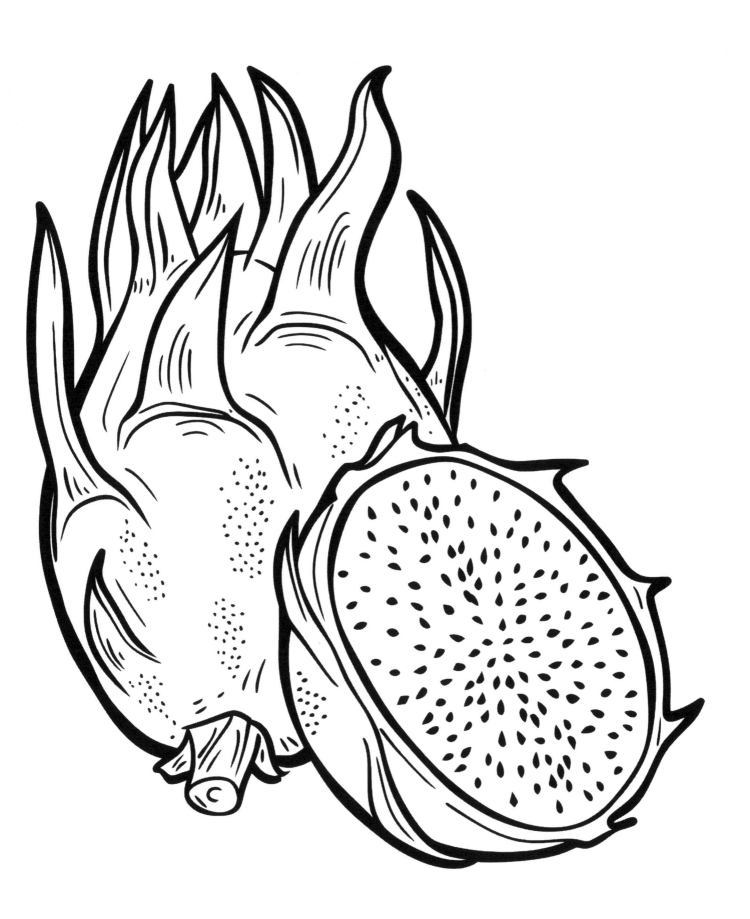

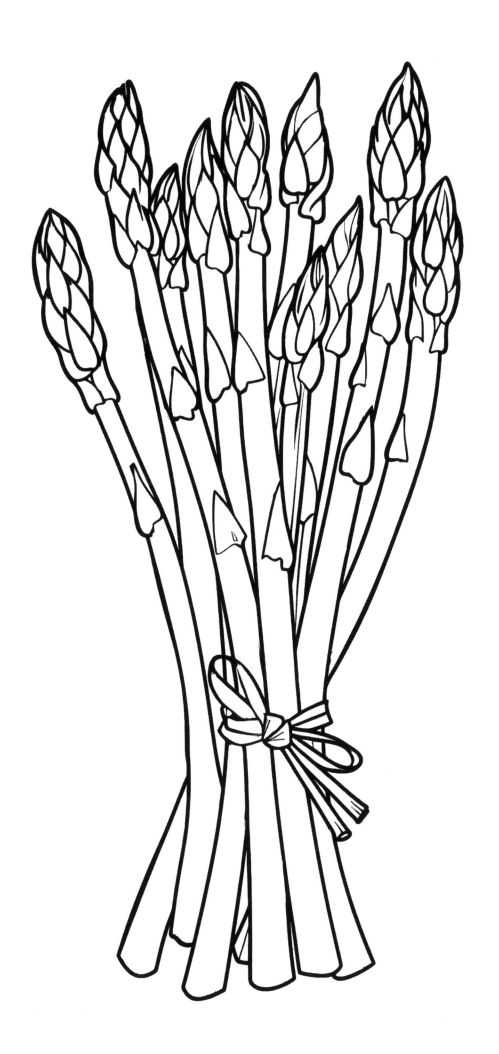

We Value Your Feedback!

Thank you for choosing our coloring book. Your experience is important to us, and we would love to hear your thoughts!
Scan the QR Code below to leave a review and let us know what you think.

How to Use the QR Code:
1. Open the camera app on your smartphone.
2. Point your camera at the QR code.
3. Tap the notification that appears to open the review link.

Thank you for your support and happy coloring!

Made in United States
Orlando, FL
03 December 2024

54890297R00061